WHO'S COUNTING?

NANCY TAFURI

SCHOLASTIC INC.

New York Toronto London Auckland Sydney

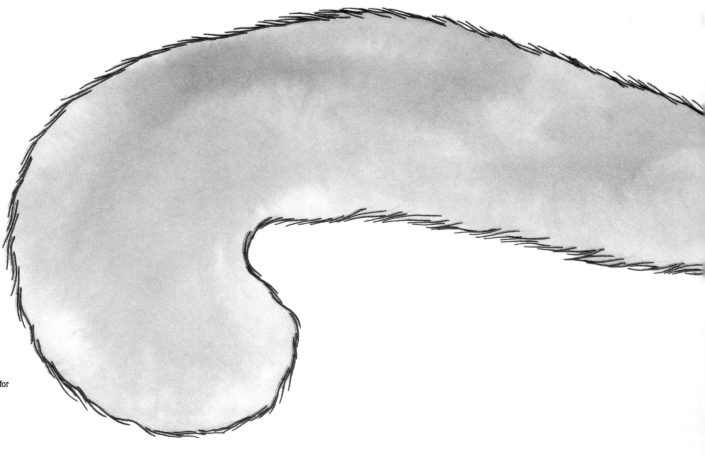

FOR ADA

A black line was combined with watercolor paints for the full-color illustrations. The text type is ITC Weiderman.

ISBN 0-590-22382-8

Copyright © 1986 by Nancy Tafuri.
All rights reserved.
Published by Scholastic Inc., 555 Broadway, New York, NY 10012, by arrangement with Greenwillow Books, a division of William Morrow & Company, Inc.

12 11 10 9 8 7 6 5 4 3 2 1   4 5 6 7 8 9/9
Printed in the U.S.A.   14
First Scholastic printing, October 1994

1 SQUIRREL

4 GEESE

5
EGGS

6 PIGLETS

7 RABBITS

8

2 BIRDS

3 MOLES

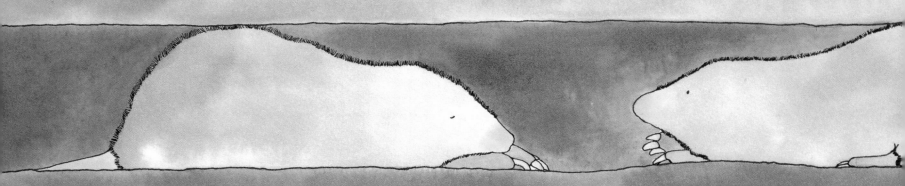

TADPOLES

9 FLOWERS

AND

10 PUPPIES-

EATING!